Lowri Madoc

R & D Business Publishing
Unit 3, Cleethorpes Business Centre,
Jackson Place,
Grimsby,
North East Lincolnshire.
DN36 4AS.

Cover Design: Eve Leoni Art

ISBN: 978-1-5272-6347-5

To Dad, Mum and John – Thank you for a very
special childhood.

CONTENTS

ACKNOWLEDGEMENTS

I would like to acknowledge and say thank you to the following people:

To Riain, Lili and Dexter for your inspiration.

To Brendan, because you know, that I know, how incredible you are.

To John Hayes for your expertise and encouragement.

.

CHAPTER ONE

It was time to say 'adios' to Northwood House for Girls for another week and 'hola' to the weekend! Don't get me wrong, I love weekly boarding at school, but I also love going home on a Friday to see what adventures are in store.

It was a chilly, grey afternoon, but grandpa and his campervan always managed to make me feel like the sun was shining. This was mostly because his old Volkswagen, his pride and joy, was literally as bright as a yellow yolk. You definitely couldn't miss him coming up the driveway. I beamed when I saw him waiting in the car park and couldn't wait to jump in.

"Presh," grandpa said. It was never 'Precious', always 'Presh'! "You all set?" My grandpa was the most unlikely campervan driver. A slight man, he always wore a suit and tie, overcoat and Russian Cossack-style winter hat — even when it was a little too warm for one! He took a lot of pride in the way he dressed and also what he drove.

I nodded enthusiastically and gave him a big hug. He helped me throw my bags into the back and I climbed up into the front seat. The front cabin area was as spotless as always and smelt of sweets. Liquorice and travel sweets to be precise.

As grandpa got in, he leant across, opened his glove compartment, pulled out a tin of Simpkins travel sweets and offered me one. I smiled, as he did this every time without fail, whether the journey was long or short. I selected a dusty pink one as always and popped it in my mouth. We liked playing the game of who could keep their sweet going for the longest.

As always, pretending to be my chauffeur, grandpa asked me, "Where would you like me to take you, madame?"

And I would ALWAYS reply, giggling with the same answer while sucking on a sweet, "The Souwf of Franth, pease, my good man." And he would always reply, "OK, my little buck-a-ninny!" That was grandpa's version of the Welsh word Bachgenne!

We go to France in the campervan every year — me, my grandparents, and a stray great auntie and uncle, all the way down to the beaches in the south.

"Travelling on the continent," as Mamgu calls it, with this lot, was brilliant. They had me rolling about with laughter, and equally riddled with embarrassment, whenever they muddled up their knowledge of foreign languages, blurting out mixed-up phrases like 'Muchas gracias, mon amie! Yow key-airo un café au lait!' loud and proud. Classic!

Today, grandpa was picking me up from boarding school not for the holidays, just for the weekend.

As he drove down the long, tree-lined driveway, away from the old main school building, my eyes followed the path that I had run earlier that week. Well, I say 'run', for me it was more like a tough walk. Cross-country running is seriously the worst PE lesson ever. It's always so cold and it was just such a long way to run.

My cheeks remained as pink as ripe peaches for two whole days after slogging my way around the grounds of Northwood on that crisp Tuesday morning. At least there were biscuits and squash served up at the end, and I didn't come last. Tanya and Emma came in another two minutes after me, linking arms and chatting. There was a cheer from the other girls in the year and the two smiled at each other for crossing the finish line together.

During my weeks at Northwood House for Girls, I share a dorm with my best friend Claire. We have so much fun. Now that we're in Year 6, we don't have to share a big dorm with the other girls; we have a whole room to ourselves and get to have some privacy.

We much prefer to be by ourselves, ever since last term when Vanessa St John, the school drama queen, accused Claire of being a thief.

Claire is a caring girl and hasn't stolen a thing in her life, let alone a limited-edition pug-shaped squishy from a friend! Vanessa, on the other hand, is a rather bitter girl with her nose in everyone else's business.

She didn't even apologise to Claire when the truth came out. She found her squishy in the bottom of her own stinky, old swim bag, underneath her bed, but because she had made such a song and dance about accusing Claire, she let her pride

get in the way. All the girls from her dorm were present and she couldn't hide it because it was disgusting. It had started to go mouldy and smelly next to the swimsuit and towel that she'd also forgotten to stick in the wash. Yuk!

Claire and I do everything together, apart from she's much better at sports than me. (She came first in cross-country, by the way.) I stick to the art room and love languages, while she sticks to the track.

Today, Claire had a hockey tournament and was then going to visit her granny on the farm. It's lambing season, so she couldn't wait to get there in time to help her uncle with the newborn lambs.

The best thing about weekly boarding is that I get to be with my friends in the week and then I can go home on a Friday to either my mum's or my dad's house.

You see, my parents are divorced, so I spend one weekend with dad and the next with mum. That way, nobody gets jealous.

Mum and dad are both actors, so they're always busy up and down the country, which is why I love going to Northwood during the week. I know it's convenient for them, too, and I do miss them, but everyone is happy and I like it this way. I like to think it's the best of both worlds. My friend, Andrea, does not get to go home every weekend as her parents live in Gibraltar. Her dad is a Captain in the Army. She only gets to see them when there is a school holiday but, does get to spend lots of time with her Grandma at weekends.

This weekend, it is my turn to visit dad. I can't wait to find out what we will be doing.

After our obligatory detour to the Shake Shop for one of their scrummy Cookies and Cream Super Shakes (with a cherry on the top), we continued on our way to dad's house.

It was 6pm and getting dark. As we got closer to the old bridge opposite dad's house, I could see the lights glowing through the windows and smoke was gently billowing out the chimney top. These were sure signs dad  was home and I couldn't wait to see him.

As we turned into the gravelled driveway, grandpa stopped for me to jump out and open the heavy, wooden, slatted gate, so that he could continue to drive in.

I dragged it over the top of the gravel, letting grandpa drive in, and then closed it fully with the wrought iron latches so that Rosie, our Yorkshire Terrier, couldn't escape.

My tummy was doing back-flips with excitement to see dad. I ran straight over to the stable-door back door of our kitchen. It was unlocked as dad was home, although I couldn't see him through the glass.

I quickly went inside and ran straight through to the hallway where I hung up my coat. Rosie wiggled over in the commando manoeuvre that she does when she's excited, and rolled on to her back, pleading for a tickle on her tummy.

She is such a brilliant and clever dog. You know, she can bark along in time to music.

She was only a few weeks old when mum was in a musical called 'Gypsy Rose Lee'. Mum's character had a dog, so she was given a puppy, just for using on stage. Mum taught her to do some really cool tricks in time to the music and looked after her in the dressing room.

The musical didn't run for long and when it ended, Rosie had no home to go to. We all couldn't bear to be without her, so we kept her.

"Who'd like a cup o' tea?" I heard grandpa call as he came in through the back door. He didn't need an answer; we're a family of tea lovers and we all like our tea with plenty of sugar. I could hear him filling up the kettle.

Dad's house is really, really old, built when Henry VIII and his wives were alive. That means that we have a lot of low ceilings with dark oak beams (the sort that people bump their heads on constantly), narrow passageways, and a really big fireplace in nearly every room.

Did you know that this type of house has horsehair in the walls?! Apparently, it was used to keep the house warm in the old days. It's really cosy and very pretty, but it doesn't have the lavish things that my friends have in their new houses, like triple glazing or underfloor heating. It can get very chilly which is why there are so many fireplaces.

Dad loves his house and all of its history, but I

just wish that it had a few more radiators. It's continuous work for dad and our handyman, as things break and fall off constantly. And because it's on a 'list' of very old houses in England, they can't make it all fancy and modern; they have to repair it to exactly the way it was before.

He fills it with stuff from his travels all over the world, some of which I like to refer to simply as 'dad's taste'; like the two-feet-tall wooden sun-god mask from South America that hangs above the fireplace in his study. Or indeed, his selection of decorated swords and knives from Asia that can't go unnoticed as you go up the stairs.

He also loves books. He has shelves and shelves of them. He's your go-to man if you need anything on languages, travel, or theatre. He even has copies of some of his books in different languages.

I knew dad was home, I just had to find him. I was about to head up to his study, thinking that was where he would be, when all of a sudden I could hear him talking loudly and intensely in the dining room. The heavy door was shut, so he obviously

11

hadn't heard grandpa or I come in. His words were all muffled through the door.

"Hang on a mo'," I thought. "That's not English he's speaking!"

The dining room is where dad normally works on his lines, preparing for his next role, so I lingered outside for a second, weighing up whether he could be disturbed or not.

There was another voice I could hear now. Then it cut off and everything went quiet.

CHAPTER TWO

I couldn't wait any longer, so I grabbed the handle and burst through the door.

Slightly startled, dad turned around and smiled.

"Hetty, cariad, you're home!" he said.

He came around from the other side of the dining table, picked me up in a bear hug and gave me a nuzzley kiss on the cheek. He knows his spikey beard bristles always make me giggle.

I must have looked a bit puzzled as I stared at him, then at the thick script and CD player on the table. I realised that the other voice must have

been on the CD.

"I'm prrarctizing my Rrrrussian!" he said with a frown and a serious Russian accent. "Vood you help me learrrrn my lines, Hetty? 'Poh-shzah-loo-stah?' That means 'please' in Russian. I'm playing a Russian detective in this new musical," he explained with a big grin.

I really, really, really love to help him with his lines, even though I get shy pretending to be the other characters. He always takes it so seriously, and whenever he puts on an accent, it is brilliant. It makes me want to crack up every time, but I try my hardest not to.

I don't think that I could ever be an actress as I would get too nervous. It must be so much fun to dress up and play other people though, but just the thought of standing in front of all those people, singing or dancing or acting, all of them STARING

AT YOU, gives me butterflies. And what if you weren't any good? They might boo you or stand up and leave. Oh no, that definitely isn't for me.

But I love that they both do this for a living. I get to visit the different theatres where my parents work and am allowed to go backstage. When I go into theatres there are always so many people busy trying to make sure their job is done so the show can go on. Children aren't allowed to wander alone, but I love seeing how it all works and where the magic is made behind the tabs.

Clever scenery and awesome lighting can really make the story come alive. When the band strikes up in the pit, I usually notice the hairs stand up on my neck. The costumes and make-up usually complete this magical experience. It's like my secret world that nobody else knows about.

These are all the parts of the theatre that I love, but what I love most is seeing my parents prepare for their roles.

My dad can speak nine different languages! Amazing, I know. I call him my 'word wizard'. He can go from playing a German soldier to an Italian baker just like that, and you would never know that he actually comes from Merthyr Tydfil in Wales.

When you listen to him speak with a foreign accent, he sounds so good. He could easily convince you that he was from that country.

He can be very cool — sometimes — apart from when he draws attention to himself in public, that is. Sometimes, I get so embarrassed that I wish I could grab a magic wand and freeze everyone. Like the time we were in the pants and vest aisle of Marks & Spencer when a tall, skinny lady stood staring at us with her mouth open.

"It's you, isn't it? That actor off the telly?" she blurted out, incredibly loudly. "Ooh, what's your name now?" she said wracking her brain. "Ooh, I loved it when you played that German in that series. Can I have a selfie? My friend Edna is a huge fan of yours."

Dad, smiling, encouraged her even more as she proceeded to give him more adoration. But then he teased her by saying, "No, my dear, you've

I was imagining how they would look — the clothes, the dance shoes, the hats. It would be exactly like Strictly Come Dancing! There was bound to be a lot of furs, as well, as it's always so cold in Russia. I was picturing thousands of gems, sequins and hand-painted costumes that would have taken months to prepare, but were obviously going to be worth it.

I had overheard dad saying there was a lot of money in this show and that they were hoping to take it to the West End. Mind you, I'm sure I heard dad say that about the last show he was in.

I helped dad practise for a while, but I was so excited that I kept stopping to ask him questions.

"So, what's your costume like? Will you have a magnifying glass to help you find clues?" I was imagining a Sherlock Holmes-type character. "Are there any children or animals in it?"

All of the best shows had children and animals in them. Mum did a pantomime last year with a real-life pony in it. It was totally awesome. The pony's name was Peach. I would nip into her (slightly pongy) penned-area, which had been made for her in a corner backstage. This was where she rested between the matinee and evening performances. I would give her a big, shiny red apple that was always thoughtfully left on a table close by.

One day, mum told me that everyone backstage was talking about the disappearing apples. I wondered what all the fuss was about. She explained that someone had been stealing the apples that were meant for the most important scene in 'Snow White' (you know, the bit where she bites into the poison apple) from the prop table.

I suddenly realised that I WAS THE APPLE SNATCHER! I felt so guilty that I was sure I now had 'APPLE THIEF' written across my forehead. I quickly learnt the importance of the backstage rule of NOT REMOVING ITEMS FROM THE PROP

TABLE!

I decided there was no need to tell anyone, but from that point onwards, I used my own pocket money to buy Peach juicy, red apples since she loved them so much.

As evening approached and I was getting into bed, dad said, "It's Saturday tomorrow. I've got a technical/dress rehearsal in the theatre so you'll be spending the day with me there. Bring your school bag and maybe you can get your homework done." He grinned and winked at me.

Ignoring the comment about the school bag, I gave him a huge smile back. "YESSSS!" I said, squeaking with delight.

Rehearsal time was so exciting, seeing every inch of the production getting ready for the opening night. It's not just the actors who have to be word and foot perfect, as without everything else happening at the right time, the show would not go on.

The best job backstage is that of the stage manager. They make sure that everyone is in the right place at the right time and wear headphones to give cues to everyone, from the musical director in the pit, to the lighting and sound guys, actors, stage crew, props organisers and wardrobe department. So many people, so many jobs.

Dad always gives me a quick lowdown on the plot as these shows can sometimes be very hard to follow. His explanations help me to understand what's going on, and then he leaves it to me to work out the ending.

"So, the show is set in Moscow, Russia, in 1985. It's about a very rich, old lady who has many people working for and looking after her. She's not very well. Actually, she's dying, and she has called for her nephews and nieces to visit her. You see, she doesn't have any children of her own. Her husband died quite young and left her all of his wealth. She's a bit of an old battle-axe, so, unfortunately, she doesn't have many friends. She only has her Chihuahuas, Olga and Petra.

"She has paid for the education of her nieces and nephews in England and feels particularly close to one of them, Niko. She thinks he's very clever, witty and that he can do no wrong, while she thinks that the other two are wrong'uns — no-good wasters. So, they come to visit her and, during their stay, some priceless jewellery goes missing. When it's discovered, not all is as it seems with Niko, the naughty nephew.

"Tomorrow, Hetty, when you've watched it, you can tell me what happens at the end."

"Hang on a sec," I thought. "Did he say CHIHUAHUAS?" Oh my goodness, those dogs are as cute as buttons. I couldn't wait to see them!

My mind started wandering. I started to wonder whether these two little doggies would need a home when the musical ended? Perhaps we could give them a nice home like we did with Rosie.

"Would they get on?" I thought.

"Nos da, cariad," dad said as he kissed me on the head. "Good night, dad," I said. "Go to sleep quickly,"

he replied, "we have to be in the theatre for 9am sharp."

I knew exactly what I was going to wear. There was only one outfit appropriate for tomorrow. It had to be my black long-sleeved t-shirt, black jeans and black trainers.

It took me a while, but I eventually drifted off to sleep, dreaming of Russian costumes… and Chihuahuas!

CHAPTER THREE

As we arrived at the bustling stage door of the Theatre Royal, there were loads of people hanging around, looking like they had been working all night. Dad said they probably had. The stage crew would have finished doing the 'get in' during the night, as the last musical finished its 'get out'.

Dad and I swerved through the crowd of smokers and coffee drinkers outside and made it to the door. Dad didn't stop to chat with anyone, he just wanted to get into work, so I followed him. Just as we were entering the building, we both received a gentle tap on the shoulder. Simultaneously we turned around. It was Keith — dad's biggest fan. Wherever dad went you could be sure to see Keith. Forever loyal Keith. Always there, a little dishevelled, programme in hand ready to be signed, and so happy to have caught dad's attention. He even seemed pleased to see me. Dad was in a hurry so couldn't stop for long, but he said he'd try and catch him for a cup of tea later. Keith looked like he could do with one.

As we went in, dad was greeted with a big 'hello Gareth, welcome back,' and was handed his dressing room key by the jolly stage door keeper, Norman (it said so on his t-shirt). He also gave me a big, toothy grin and asked me to sign in in the visitors' book.

"She looks like you, hey, Gareth," he said. "Spitting image!" "Do you think so?" dad replied, giving me a big grin.

Oh my god, I get so embarrassed when that happens. I gave Norman a very shy smirk.

You know, stage door keepers are very interesting. They never ever come out from behind the glass (perhaps only to use the loo!), I'm sure of it. It doesn't matter which theatre you're in, they all seem the same.

I was looking at Norman and all of the things behind the glass hatch. He has such a cool job as nobody can get into the theatre unless the stage door keeper says so. That is why it's essential you're nice to them at all times, my mum would say.

Was it possible the stage door keepers actually lived at the stage door? Perhaps they slept there every night, keeping an eye on the theatre 24/7. I mean, there was everything one could ever need in their little rooms: an obligatory tatty, old, comfy armchair for snoozing, a kettle, toaster, tin of biscuits, cups, spoons, teabags, milk bottles kept on the windowsill, and, of course, an old-fashioned radio that was ALWAYS playing Radio 2.

Then, of course, there were the tools of the trade: a big, numbered, wooden key-holder with keys for all of the dressing rooms, a really cool panel of buttons to open various doors to let staff and visitors into the backstage area, and a telephone on a huge switchboard that connected to all of the dressing rooms.

There would also be a collection of security chains hanging on the wall, which were kept there during the day and then put on the emergency exits late at night when everyone had left the building. I know this because one day, in my mum's last show, the on-duty fireman told me all about what he did.

And lastly, there would be a box with a button on it that also had a long, thin, mic attached to it. When the stage door keeper pressed the button and spoke into it, he could be heard throughout the entire backstage area. It was like the control centre; the heart of the whole theatre. I think I want to be a stage door keeper when I'm older.

It was 8.50am and felt like Piccadilly Circus in the small entrance. Norman had given me a visitor sticker, a biscuit and, most importantly, the wi-fi code.

Although the cast all knew each other from

rehearsals, today they were meeting new people who worked backstage.

Whether it is old faces or new, a theatre is always a lively place to be.

In the corridors, there were glamorous young dancers stretching and laughing together, while the actors walked calmly through, keen to find their dressing rooms.

And then there was the stage crew. You knew who they were because they were dressed all in black so they couldn't be seen by the audience when they moved the scenery around on stage between scenes. They were also camouflaged in the wings, which is why I had chosen the right clothes to wear today.

The dock doors were open and the last pieces of scenery were being carefully lifted in by the men in black.

As I walked through, trying to remain inconspicuous, I was hit by so many smells. There was a strong stench of glue, paint and freshly sawn plywood, but when I turned the other way, there was an intense waft of deodorants, hairsprays, make-up, and… ironing. I could smell the steam and starch coming from down the corridor.

There were tannoy speakers dotted along the corridor through which I could hear the orchestra warming up.

I followed closely behind dad down the corridor towards the stairs. His dressing room key fob said 'No. 1', which was on the first floor. As I peered up the stairwell, I could see there were four more floors of dressing rooms. It seemed huge. A big cast means a big theatre.

Next to dad's dressing room were four other rooms, including another big one at the end of the corridor. Through a crack in the door of a brightly-lit room, I could see quite a few wigs on mannequin heads.

Dad's room was quite bare, although this wasn't unusual. Mum's dressing rooms always seemed to be filled with so much more stuff: flowers, make-up, perfume, cards, etc. Dad's were always less fussy.

The typical big light bulbs you see in the movies surrounded three large mirrors, which were placed alongside a dressing table that ran the full length of one side of the room.

There were a few clothes hanging up, a couple of pairs of shoes underneath that had been left by the wardrobe department, a few items of make-up that had been left by the make-up lady, and a false moustache that had been pinned to a mannequin head.

Dad put his bag down and got out his script and pen. His costume dresser came in with a big 'hello!' and his freshly pressed shirt, which she hung up for him. The stage manager then announced over the tannoy that all cast members were required on the stage in five minutes.

I slumped on the big, comfy sofa while dad quickly got changed in the ensuite. He came out looking handsome in a dark-grey suit, white shirt, tie, and shiny, black shoes.

He sat at his dressing table and got started by brushing his upper lip with the spirit gum. I could smell it. YUCK! He applied his moustache and then put on a little bit of brown make-up with a sponge.

"Ready?" he said. "Come on, bring your school bag with you. You're gonna sit out front. Got your phone?" he said sarcastically as I waved it at him.

He always teases me by saying that my phone is glued to my hand. I had already entered the wi-fi code. I took a selfie of me and dad and sent it to

him, and then another one to Claire.

Outside his dressing room, we followed the sign pointing to 'THE STAGE'.

As he opened the heavy door, I followed him through. The temperature fell and I was suddenly covered in goosebumps.

I felt a thrill of excitement as we headed into the darkness of the stage area. I was met with long, black cloths hanging down from the flies above and the muffled noise of busy people in every direction.

As my eyes adjusted and I moved further forwards into the side of the stage, there they all were. Stage workers were tinkering with the lights, some were making finishing touches to the scenery with paint brushes and tools, while others were arranging props and small areas for the actors' quick costume changes.

Some had headphones with microphones attached and were speaking to others around the stage area. It was like a small village of creators, all doing their bit for the big event.

Dad led the way, past the stage manager's prompt desk and through another door. I didn't want to lose sight of dad, but I really wanted to stay and watch them all doing their work.

This door took us through a short passage, then finally out to the front of house. It was much brighter and much more beautiful than backstage. Everything was painted gold and red and had fancy velvet-like wallpaper.

Ahead, I could see the toilets and a bar for the customers, and the double doors were open to the huge auditorium. It was massive, especially so as it was completely empty of an audience.

As I walked through to the circle seating, above I could see 'the gods', and below a vast stalls area. Wow, this was a big theatre. At least 1,800 seats I thought to myself.

I took a picture; I had to send it to Claire.

Dad helped me find a seat in Row H (it was always a better view a few rows back from the front), then kissed me goodbye and reminded me to do some homework.

Apart from the director and various assistants, I was the only one sat in the auditorium. Unfortunately, this meant that people kept coming over and checking on me.

First, it was the female choreographer, then a

front of house manager, and then a cleaner. They were all very nice, offering me sweets an' all, but it's just so embarrassing.

Shyly, I said 'thank you', but then I sat down quickly, making as little eye contact as possible.

On stage, the cast was being led through a warm-up. I reluctantly pulled my books out of my bag and half-heartedly thought about making a start on my maths homework.

I glared at the algebra book but was easily distracted. I could hear the director talking to another lady next to her. There was tension in the air. The pressure was mounting.

I had overheard dad talking on the phone yesterday about the investors. They were coming on opening night and it had to be right.

Many of the cast members were worried about their lines as they had had only had two weeks of rehearsals, and there had been complaints about the bad quality of sound in the theatre.

"What good is a musical if you can't hear it

properly?" I heard someone comment.

The musical director in the pit was waving his stick to show the director that he was ready to start. She took her cue and, through a mic, asked everyone to get ready for the opening number.

The cast cleared the stage and a stunning, heavy, red curtain came down. This meant they were REALLY ready!

As the house lights went down and it became dark in the auditorium, I waited for a while until everyone was well and truly engrossed in their jobs and focused on the stage.

The band started up and as the curtain went up, a beautiful setting of Moscow town took over the stage.

I watched for a few minutes, admiring the beauty, then decided that while it was dark and nobody would spot me, I'd quickly nip backstage.

CHAPTER FOUR

I went back out through the double doors of the auditorium and headed towards the door that dad had brought me through earlier. I pushed it a fraction, allowing my eyes to adjust as I tried to remain as quiet as a little stage mouse.

A loud 'whoooooosh!' came from a black box that was on the floor very near to me and suddenly it was pumping out beautiful, white smoke in the direction of the stage. The dry ice gave an even greater chill to the air.

Pleased to be dressed in black, I snuck, undetected, past the stage manager at the prompt desk, which was all aglow with buttons and lights. There were others milling around her, too, so I confidently blended into the black backdrop.

I crept silently down the side of the wings and then through the door to the corridor where dad's dressing room was. 'Phew!' I thought, his door was closed, so I sidled towards the stairwell.

Unfortunately, children like me weren't meant to be wandering around backstage. Health and safety rules are very strict in theatres. Wherever I looked, there were hazard warning signs.

Mum and dad always warned me about never touching ANYTHING backstage. They reminded me of the rules all the time!

THEATRE RULES FOR CHILDREN:

1. **DO NOT TOUCH ANY BUTTONS OR SWITCHES — OR YOU COULD DIE!**
2. **DO NOT GO ON TO THE STAGE WITHOUT A PARENT — OR YOU COULD DIE!**
3. **IF YOU ARE EVER IN THE WINGS OR ON STAGE, DO NOT TOUCH ANY ROPES, PULLIES, STAGE WEIGHTS, PROPS, BOTTLES**

OF LIQUIDS, LIGHTS, SOUND EQUIPMENT, ANY EQUIPMENT, OR ANY OF THE SCENERY. IN FACT, DON'T TOUCH ANYTHING THAT DOESN'T BELONG TO YOU — OR YOU COULD DIE!

The rules were going around and around in my head and I knew I wasn't meant to be here; I was meant to be in my seat at the front of house.

Butterflies were doing back-flips in my tummy, but I thought, seeing as I was here now, nobody would mind if I popped up to the chorus girls' dressing room... would they?

The chorus girls were all on stage about to do the first scene, so they wouldn't need to know. I wouldn't touch anything dangerous; I only wanted to go and have a quick look at their costumes.

As my butterflies were trying to drag me back towards Row H, I decided it was okay to ignore them. What could possibly go wrong?

Apprehensively, I headed up the stairs. As soon as I had commenced my ascent, another girl came rushing down.

Panic-stricken, I could only hope I would somehow become invisible, but I knew that it was a ridiculous thought that only happened in places like Hogwarts!

As she charged towards me, she spoke. "Hello, you wouldn't happen to have seen a green velvet handbag anywhere, would you?" said the girl, who unfortunately could definitely see me, but clearly didn't seem bothered.

"No, sorry," I said.

She went around me. "Please keep your eyes peeled for it. It's for Madam Pavlova," she said with a smile and slight hint of frustration. "She's going to get really cross at me again. I'm going to get the blame again. Things keep going missing and I'm sure she'll blow her top soon!"

She had a friendly, gentle look about her, but she was definitely concerned.

"Good luck," I muttered as she hurtled on down the remaining stairs and along the corridor towards the stage entrance.

For some reason, the dancers' dressing rooms were always the furthest from the stage. This always seemed odd to me as they seemed to be on the stage the most.

I knew I had to go up, right to the top. As I did, that smell I loved got stronger: the mixture of body sprays, aftershaves, perfumes, and make-up. It was like a magical mist luring me forward.

The door to the first dressing room on the third floor was open. There were enough seats and mirrors for about 10 girls, all with their own dressing table area.

Each had a small towel with their make-up laid out, including a set of false eyelashes, as well as loads of brushes, hairsprays and potions. There were 'good luck' cards and trinkets from

their families… and their BOYFRIENDS!

In a trance-like state, I let my senses lead me around the room, not touching — just gently stroking — some of the shimmery items in front of me. The glamour of this room was so overwhelmingly beautiful, my mind had drifted into a daydream.

A loud announcement on the tannoy poked me out of my musing.

"Could Julie, that's Julie the dresser, please come to the stage immediately. Thank you."

"Oh dear," I thought. "That was probably Julie I met on the stairs."

I turned and pushed the door so that it wasn't quite closed. As I did, I froze, aghast at all of the costumes on various rails stationed around the room. There were rows of sparkly and embellished skirts, tops, jackets, dresses, boots, shoes, hats, and mittens, and a lot of fake furs.

They were put in order and had been labelled by the wardrobe department, Act 1 and Act 2.

There was one costume still hanging on the Act 1 rail. It was a beautiful dress, shimmering with layers of gold fabrics and stunning sequins. Like a magnet it pulled me closer.

It had to be a spare one. I couldn't believe it. Perhaps this visit to the dressing room was meant to be and this costume was waiting here for me to find it?

Theatre rules aside for a moment, I reached up and pulled the dress off the hanger. I stood there,  holding it up against me, staring and admiring myself in the mirror.

It was a bit big, but I unzipped the back of the beautiful dress and stepped into it. Over my own black clothes, I pulled up the sleeves.

I studied the sleeves and the length of the skirt. Standing tall, shoulders back whilst trying to look as elegant as I could, I pondered a moment at myself.

There was a head-dress on the dressing table beside me, so I placed that on my head too. I also spotted some dancing shoes and quickly pointed my toes as I slipped my feet into them.

Everything fit. I was meant to try the entire outfit on.

There were mirrors on every wall. As my arms hugged my waist, I smiled at myself. I liked the feeling of being in the costume and I couldn't believe how different I looked. I mean, it was definitely me looking back at myself in the mirror. I stared and stared. I looked a little older.

I grabbed my phone and took a selfie. Claire was never going to believe this.

Through the tannoy, I could hear the orchestra

playing and the actors talking. Not paying much attention to it and still mesmerised by the way I looked, I began to forget where I was and how much trouble I would be in if someone saw me. The imp in me was enjoying herself.

While checking myself out and taking a selfie, posed with my hip sticking out to one side and pulling a daft face, a knock at the door made me jump and promptly gave that imp a warning. I stood up straight and put my phone behind my back as if I had just been caught by a teacher.

A friendly looking boy poked his head around the door. "You coming or what? We'd better be quick before the boss knows we're late. We need to be ready for scene two!"

He winked with a cheeky grin and then grabbed my hand. Together, we ran down the stairs.

Running while being dragged, and definitely not wanting to be late for the boss, I was wondering if the boy really thought I was a dancer. Did he not realise I was Gareth's daughter and that I should absolutely not be in this costume?

Before I could stop to find out, we were careering down the stairs.

"You're not meant to run. Health and safety!" I blurted out, nervously giggling inside my stomach.

I don't think he heard me as he just continued.

As he pulled on the heavy door to enter the side of the stage, it was dark, and black cloths hung at the edges of the scenery.

My eyes took a second to adjust again and register the cast members standing at the side of the stage, waiting for their cues to go on.

Dodging people and stage weights on the floor, I found myself a place to stand so that 1) I wasn't in the way, 2) nobody would really see me, and 3) I could take a moment to assess the situation I was now in.

What was I DOING?

"Stay calm," I thought, "and I'll find a moment to escape back up to the dressing room and put the costume back where I found it."

The bright lights on the stage were like a bursting sunrise that showed off the costumes beautifully. Madam Pavlova shimmered and sparkled in golds, creams and lace. The dancers who were playing butlers and servants in the opening scene looked pristine and elegant and their dancing was superb.

The director kept stopping to make changes to the lighting and sound. The actors were given a few notes and told to move to the left or to the right so that it looked better.

The lady playing Madame Pavlova, Maria, came on and off the stage a few times and didn't seem very happy at all.

As it was so quiet in the wings, I could hear every word she was saying. She was getting very cross at the girl I met on the stairs, Julie, her dresser.

"Water. I need water!" she said with a grimace.

She went on. "And that followspot operator

needs his eyes checked. The light is never on me when it should be!"

She hadn't finished. "And that dry ice is killing my throat. I can't get my notes out."

As I watched, Julie did not shout back. Instead, she politely smiled, pulled up a chair for her and said she would get her some water straight away.

Maria was still grumbling and complaining to herself as Julie disappeared.

"How rude and what dreadful manners," I thought. She couldn't speak to Julie like that. It was wrong.

CHAPTER FIVE

I had totally forgotten my own predicament as I sat eavesdropping and watching in awe of Julie. As I did so, I looked around at my surroundings.

Every inch of the stage fascinated me: the lights above with the different coloured filters creating the perfect glow on stage, the network of metal balconies above me, from where the men in black walked and operated the stage effects and, the rig with multiple ropes and pullies hung.

There were sandbags and stage weights dotted around the floor, all keeping the scenery in place. Behind me were buttons and switches and a huge red leaver for the safety curtain. Everything was in its place and everything was there for a reason, like a magnificent machine.

Something near the prop table caught my eye. It was the shimmering collars of the two Chihuahuas.

The dogs were right there, in a super luxurious cage. I couldn't believe it. Even the dogs knew how to behave within this well-oiled engine.

Curled up together, they looked adorable. I went to move towards them, but stepped back to my safe spot as a lady in black walked up to them and opened the cage door to give them a loving pat.

From the table above, she took a handful of little treats and gave each of them a couple. One of the other men in black

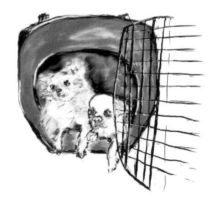

tapped her on the shoulder and then they both went to help move the scenery for the next scene change.

I had to take a photo of them for Claire. Better still, I'd take a video.

I crouched down and got my phone out. I zoomed in and got a close-up of their tiny little faces. As I did, one of the dogs pushed the cage door open.

Oh no! The lady had forgotten to lock their cage door.

Again, I went to move towards them, but I stepped back behind the black curtain as someone else walked by.

Oh no! As I feared, one of the dogs got out of the cage and then the other followed. They didn't run away. Instead, these dogs seemed to know exactly where they were going.

They looked up to the table where the treats were. Both of them quickly pitter-pattered on their tiny paws towards a box. One of them jumped up on to the box, then on to a chair, and then up on to the top of the table. I couldn't believe it. It was like an act on 'Britain's Got Talent'.

They were there for what seemed like only a few seconds and then they went back down the same way with their mouths full of treats and what looked like a string of beads. It must have been one of their toys.

"Amazing! Golden buzzer stuff!" I thought as they headed back into their sumptuous beds in the cage.

The stage lights dimmed and it went very dark all around me. Only the safety strips on the floor could be seen for a moment.

As the machine started up, the scenery was removed and a different set was moved smoothly into its place. The orchestra continued to play as the lights came up on a beautiful scene of a glittering staircase, just what you'd imagine the inside of a palace to look like.

Then came Maria, chatting to someone else, complaining again.

"My dressing room is so far away and those stairs are no good for my knees," she said, unsatisfied.

They were heading for the prop table by the Chihuahuas. Maria stopped and stared. She searched the table but she could not find what she was looking for.

She started to get even more cross than before. Her fuming face and puffed-up cheeks were surely about to explode. Whatever it was that she couldn't find, it was making her boil over.

With all her energy, she turned and stomped on to the stage, nearly knocking the other lady over in the process. With her dress swishing in sync with her heavy, angry steps, she stood right in the middle of the stage, waving her arms about, causing the orchestra to come to an untuneful halt.

"**STOP, STOP, STOP! I CAN'T CARRY ON LIKE THIS!**" she started shouting frantically. "I now cannot find my **PEARLS!** They are not on the **PROP TABLE. NOTHING SHOULD BE REMOVED FROM THE PROP TABLE!** This is ridiculous! The **PEARLS** are the main prop. The whole show is based around the pearls being stolen!"

All of a sudden, you couldn't hear a single gemstone drop. The entire theatre fell silent.

The smooth, well-oiled machine had come to a screeching standstill. Even those on the rigs above stopped and peered on to the stage to see what was going on.

The stage manager wasn't sure what to do next. Then, a voice from the front of house spoke through one of the mics. It was the director.

"Uhh, okay, Maria. Let's see if we can sort this out. Julie, darling. Are you there, Julie? Please could you come out here for a second?"

A very timid-looking Julie stepped out from the wings and on to the stage. She stood with her head down and was obviously so embarrassed.

I really felt sorry for her and wanted to tell Maria to stop bullying her and be kind. But I didn't. I couldn't. By now, Maria was looking like a puffed-up pumpkin.

"Julie, do you know where the pearls are, darling? So that we can carry on with the show," said the director, slightly exasperated.

"I promise I put them on the table before the show started, but they are not there now," Julie said.

Oh no, no, no! I quickly realised what had happened and that I was the only one who knew the truth. What was I going to do?

The butterflies were now going crazy in my tummy, willing me out of the door and back up to the dressing room. But I knew I needed to do something. I couldn't leave poor Julie to take the blame for something she hadn't done. I even had the evidence on my phone.

As the discussion continued on stage, I gathered up all of my brave bones and squeezed my eyes tight for a second, wishing myself luck.

I didn't have time to think any longer, so I stepped out from behind the stage tabs.

"Excuse me," I said in a disappointingly meek voice.

I was cross with myself. "If you were brave enough to step out, then speak up, girl," I told myself.

"Excuse me," I repeated a little more confidently. "I think I know what happened to the pearls."

The silence was excruciating. Julie and Maria turned to look upstage towards me with very confused faces. They weren't the only ones. I could feel eyes staring at me from all corners of the stage.

Strangely, I could see nothing of the auditorium. It was in complete darkness.

"The dogs have them!" I said. I knew how ridiculous it sounded, but I carried on. "I promise you; the dogs have them. I saw them take a few items from the prop table."

Thankfully, the ridiculousness of what I was saying distracted me from the fact that they weren't quite sure who I was.

The boy who dragged me down from the dressing room ran over to the Chihuahuas and opened the door. He put his hand in and took out the pearls.

He ran back on to the stage and handed them to Maria. He then winked at me as he went back to his position.

Maria turned to Julie and looked stunned and equally embarrassed.

Julie looked at me, smiled, and mouthed the words 'thank you'.

After a silence that seemed to last forever, Maria plucked up her courage and spoke.

"I'm… I'm sorry, Julie," said Maria, ashamed. I think she was absorbing all of the fuss that she had made around her.

The director's voice came from the darkness of the auditorium and said, "Thank you, darling. I'm so pleased we've found them. Can we get on with the show now?"

And that's exactly what everyone did.

As we left the stage and people shuffled around to find their correct positions to carry on, I saw Maria take Julie's hand and apologise to her once again. She seemed to really mean it.

They both smiled at each other and Julie handed Maria some water. They both looked relieved.

The stage manager came over and said thank you to me for helping to solve the mystery. I showed her the video on my phone and she couldn't believe how clever the dogs were, either. She said she was going to make a sign for their cage door that said, 'Please Keep Cage Door Closed'.

While in the euphoria of helping to solve the lost props conundrum, my mind quickly switched to dad. Had he seen everything that had just happened?

In the darkness of the wings, I saw him coming from the side of the stage through the door nearest to his dressing room. He was heading towards me and the stage manager.

As he came closer, I stood at an angle so that he couldn't fully see my face. He thankfully spoke to the stage manager, instead.

"What was all the commotion just then? What drama did I miss?"

The stage manager explained what had happened, indicating that I had helped solve the problem. Dad, not recognising me, gave me a congratulatory pat on my shoulder and thankfully  couldn't chat any longer as his cue to go on stage was coming up.

I took my cue to exit the stage.

CHAPTER SIX

My heart was pounding. How was that all possible? I felt like Cinderella at the ball, as if a little magic had carried me through the whole experience.

My luck and time were about to expire, too. As I ran up the stairs, with no hesitation this time, my nerves, relief and exhaustion made me feel giddy as I reached the top.

As I entered the dressing room, checking that nobody had returned before me, I went in and stood by one of the full-length mirrors. I stared at myself for one last time, taking in the thrill of truly disguising myself.

I smiled and took one more selfie for Claire.

On the tannoy, I could hear the scene had just finished, so I knew I didn't have long until the dancers would be back for their next outfits.

As I took a deep breath, I quickly pulled my arms out of the top and removed the rest of the clothes, trying to make sure that I put everything back in the exact places I had found them: the shoes, the headdress and the dress. Then, I made sure my phone was in my back pocket.

I could hear footsteps pounding rapidly up the stairs, so I nipped out of the dressing room to the ladies' toilet across the corridor. I closed the door quietly and waited until everyone had gone into their dressing rooms. I then made my escape back down the stairs and back to the side of the stage.

As I made my way through, staying out of everyone's way, I saw the dogs with their cage door firmly closed. Maria and Julie were chatting to each other as Julie helped her zip up her dress, making sure that everything was just right.

On stage, Maria sang the most fantastic song to another actor who was playing her nephew.

The show seemed to be running smoothly. It all felt a little less stressed and they were all enjoying their jobs.

I watched the stage manager giving her cues. I was transfixed at all she did and commanded. I was thinking. Perhaps I'll be a stage manager when I'm older. As the glow on the stage went from very bright to low lighting, in the dimness I headed back to the front of house.

I followed the same path back to find my seat in Row H. When I got there and sat back down, I was breathless from nerves but relieved. Dad was on stage. I sat very still and watched.

I love to watch him work. The scene was very moving and I could feel tears

pooling in the corner of my eyes.

Madame Pavlova's family were gathered by her bedside, all pretending to love and adore her, but really, they were hoping to be told how much money they would be getting from her when she died.

Speaking with a strong Russian accent, Detective Smirkov (aka dad) explained she had been betrayed by her beloved nephew, Niko. He was a fraud and had stolen a lot of money from her over the years, and it was he who had stolen the jewels.

As I listened, I looked up to the ceiling so that my tears would drain away. I was not going to cry; that would be ridiculous.

Thankfully, Olga and Petra, the dogs, came on stage to lighten the mood and drain the tears away. They were superstars. They were her loyal pups. They even barked in time to the music, just like my Rosie. So clever!

The rest of the show was brilliant and as they all came on for the final curtain call to take their bow, I stood up when my dad came on. He really did make the best Russian detective.

As the actors left the stage and everyone finished for a break, I put my school bag on my shoulder. Suddenly, there was a hand placed firmly on my shoulder.

"Oh no!" I thought.

I froze with fear, thinking someone had spotted that I wasn't in my seat for a lot of the show and that they were going to tell me off for wandering around on my own.

"Would you like me to show you backstage to your dad's dressing room, Hetty?" said the front of house manager.

"Sure," I said, relieved.

I followed her through the doors I was now familiar with as if I had no idea where I was going and followed her to dad's dressing room. I knocked and waited in case he was still changing, but he answered for me to go in.

I plonked down on to dad's big, comfy sofa

and watched him take off his make-up and the false moustache. He was asking me about the show and what I thought of it.

"I loved the dogs, dad. They were so clever!" I said.

He looked at me and gave me a funny smile. "And what about the rest of it? Did you enjoy the story? Did you like the actors and the singing?" he said.

I think he wanted me to say whether I liked his performance in it and if I thought he was good or not. He always wanted to know what I thought. "Yes, it was really good, dad. Can I watch it again? I liked your Russian accent."

He nodded and said he had a break now, but that there was another dress rehearsal later that evening.

"Did you get your homework done?" dad said.

"Ummm, no, sorry, not yet," I said, a little embarrassed.

"What were you doing all that time?" he said.

I wanted to tell him so much, but I didn't.

"Come on, let's go around to The Blue Parrot café and have that cup of tea with Keith. You can get it done there."

Dad was chatting away as he put on his shoes, combed his hair and grabbed his jacket. "But what did you think of the real detective today, Hetty?" he said.

Not quite sure what he meant, my heart began racing. "What do you mean, dad?" I replied, not knowing if I had actually been rumbled or not.

"You know, the girl who discovered the truth about the missing props. She was the real hero of the day, don't you think?"

As I began to go beetroot-red, he went on. "Not only did she discover the truth behind the disappearing jewellery, but she was also brave enough to tell everyone the truth. She made sure that the blame wasn't put on the wrong person. After that, I didn't hear anyone blaming anyone for anything else."

I was pleased that he was so impressed, but I couldn't look him in the eye. Did he suspect something?

"Uhh, yes, I suppose you're right, dad. She did solve the mystery of the day. Did you catch her name?" I said, with my fingers crossed behind my back, hoping he'd confirm he didn't have a clue who she was.

"No, no, I didn't," he said, pausing. "It was one of the dancers."

I changed the subject quickly and said to dad that I needed some help with my algebra homework. I didn't, but my butterflies were grateful to be leaving through the stage door as we hurried over to get a seat at The Blue Parrot café.

CHAPTER SEVEN

Early on Monday morning, dad and I left his house and drove back to school.

I was still reliving my breathtaking trip to the theatre in my head. It was so dreamlike and most of all, I cannot believe that I, Hetty Jones, went out on stage and spoke in front of so many people. Where did I find that courage?

"So, cariad, you're going to mum's next weekend and I will see you in two weeks' time," dad said with a chirpy smile.

"The next time grandpa picks you up, he'll be bringing you to Bristol," he explained.

'Babushka' was touring around the country, so each week the show visited a different town and set up in a new theatre.

"I've got great digs. You're gonna love them," he said, promisingly.

I listened intently to dad's description, as some of the digs where he chose to stay

were better than others. You see, actors don't like to spend a lot of money on fancy digs if they can help it and I was keen to know where I would be staying.

He told me he would be staying in a rented room in a lady's house near to the theatre. He said he had stayed there before and that it was a nice, big place with a huge garden. Plus, the landlady had a dog!

I thought this sounded pretty good, so I gave him a big grin of approval.

It was nearly 8.30am when we arrived at school. Dad gave me the biggest hug and a kiss and walked me into the boarding house.

The boarding house mistress, Miss Lane, always stopped to say hello to dad when he came inside.

Miss Lane was about 40 years old and quite pretty, but she always wore brown clothes. Whenever she chatted to dad, she would remove her glasses that were perched on the end of her nose and start acting a bit 'girly'. This morning was no exception.

"Here we go," I thought.

Dad, of course, beamed back at her and was very chatty and charming, leaving me rosy-red and embarrassed, yet again.

I told dad I needed to hurry up as the bell was

about to go and that I needed to put my things in my dorm, but really I just wanted him to leave. Thankfully, after I gave him a big hug and a kiss on the cheek, he did. Although I knew I was going to miss him, I couldn't wait to see him in a couple of weeks and watch 'Babushka' again..

I raced upstairs as I knew Claire would be there. Her grandma always dropped her back at the school for 8am.

I flung the door open and threw my bags on to my bed. Claire was already there, folding away her own clothes and putting her pyjamas under her pillow, ready for later.

I couldn't wait to share all that had happened to me that weekend. I knew I could trust her with all my secrets.

We both jumped on to my bed and immediately pulled out our phones to start showing each other our photos. I was also dying to see the pictures of the baby lambs.

She started to tell me about how she had helped her uncle deliver the lambs. They were up until 3am with the vet and delivered four of them, and there were still more to come over the next few days. It sounded exhausting but also so exciting.

Her uncle even let her name the first two that were born. So, she did: Hetty and Claire.

"Awwwwwwwww," I said. "That's adorable!"

No sooner had we gotten comfy than the bell rang. This meant we had to get to registration in five minutes. We grabbed our school bags and chased down the stairs together.

We dashed out from the boarding house, across the car park and past the sports hall. We were in the same tutor group, so we went inside and sat down for registration.

Mr Bennett came in, put down his towering pile of papers, and took the register. He seemed excited about a new inter-house competition that he wanted volunteers for. It was a public speaking competition.

Normally I would literally run a mile, as I steer clear of anything like this, as it means standing up in front of people and talking. The thought of being stared at by a large crowd was not appealing to me, to say the least.

But I really liked Mr Bennett and that morning I felt a little different. He always had 100% enthusiasm for these competitions and always really encouraged us to participate. So, I listened to what the competition involved.

He said we could choose any subject we wanted to talk about, but there needed to be a kind of message of mindfulness within it. We could talk about something we had done, seen, or experienced, or perhaps something that we had found emotional and touching.

I would usually have my arm well and truly glued down by my side, but this time I started to think I might be able to do this. Where had my desire to stand up and talk in front of people come from?

It was because I knew exactly what I would like to talk about. I really wanted to tell them all about what had happened to me when I put on one of the costumes, when I spotted the dogs stealing the props, and when I managed to save the wrong person from getting blamed.

I knew it sounded ridiculous, that they wouldn't believe me and that I couldn't say a word in front of a crowd, anyway. But then I realised this sort of thing happens all the time. Even here at our boarding house.

If friends are under pressure or stressed and overreact to things, they can get so cross and blame others. Losing your head is really easy to do, but we've got to learn to stay calm, talk to our friends and always tell the truth.

We have to be brave and stick up for our friends, as well as sometimes admitting that we are wrong. Saying sorry can really help, too.

I knew exactly the message I wanted to deliver in my speech. Kindness, honesty and forgiveness were the messages I really wanted to share.

With some stirring, new-found confidence, I put my hand up to volunteer.

Claire looked at me with sheer astonishment and concern. She asked if I was sure, as she knew this wasn't usually my cup of tea and was probably concerned I might let House down.

I whispered to her that I wanted to give it a go. "Don't worry Claire, I've got this," I said way-too confidently.

Mr Bennett was surprised, too, but he was beaming. He went on about how pleased he was that I had volunteered and come out of my comfort zone. He was gushing and going on a bit. I hate it when adults do that, it's so embarrassing.

It took me a few days to write my speech as we only had a week to prepare. There were four girls speaking in total, one from each house.

As D Day approached, and I was going to have to deliver a speech in front of what seemed like thousands of people, Mr Bennett gave us all a chance to practise in front of him. This was so he could give us tips on our delivery. I was starting to regret my bravery, so I was very glad to have his expertise.

"Hetty, it's a great speech and a great message. Stay focused, look at your audience and practise reading it aloud. That way, you will get to know your speech well and you won't have to look down at your notes all of the time," he said so enthusiastically.

So, I did. I practised and practised and practised until I knew it off by heart.

"And anyway," I thought, "what am I worried about? It's only 300 girls I've got to speak in front of."

With one eyebrow raised, I chuckled to myself as I knew there was a lot to be concerned about.

The morning of the competition came. Claire knew I was nervous and gave me a chocolate digestive biscuit as a gift of good luck. I didn't want to practise in front of her as I knew that I'd get embarrassed. Odd, I know, as 300 others awaited me in the hall.

As my turn came, I walked up to the podium in front of the whole school and, trying not to look as fearful as I felt inside, I placed my notes in front of me.

I took a deep breath to calm myself and began.

The whole school was silent, looking at me. I just kept going and kept thinking, "**STAY FOCUSED, BE BRAVE!**"

Even though the corner of my mouth developed an uncontrollable twitch, I managed to get through it. I mentioned no names and no specific incidents, but the message seemed to be heard.

When I finished, the whole hall cheered and clapped. I did it! Inside I was punching the sky. It felt good. I sat back and listened to the other girls deliver their brilliant speeches. I know I was bright red in the face, but I couldn't have been happier.

After the speeches were finished and before the winners were announced, each house served up cake and squash for the girls.

Claire put her arm around my shoulder and gave me a squeeze. Other girls in my house seemed to really like my speech, too. I was just relieved that it was over..

As we were chatting, Vanessa St John pushed her way through the crowd towards me and Claire with her shoulders.

"Was that speech aimed at me?" she said, looking at me with pursed lips and scrunched up eyes.

"No, why do you think that?" I replied, delighted it had touched her squishy-gate nerve.

"Well," she said, looking at Claire and then down at the ground. "I'm sorry for not saying sorry to you," she blurted out.

I couldn't believe it.

"I know you didn't steal my squishy," she added quickly.

Well, how about that

then? She found her bravery and apologised to Claire.

I could see that Claire was so happy.

"Apology accepted," Claire replied, and I gave Vanessa a congratulatory pat on the shoulder.

The head mistress, Mrs Williams, presented me with a runner-up trophy. I may not have come first, but Vanessa St John had already made me feel like the real winner today.

HETTY'S GLOSSARY

Buck-a-ninny/Bachgenne – Welsh for young girl

Mamgu – Welsh for grandma

Prop table – This is where all the props (theatrical property) or objects that each actor uses during a show, are laid out clearly marked.

Dress rehearsal – this is a full-scale rehearsal where the actors and musicians perform every detail of the performance. This is normally in full costume with props.

Pit – this is the orchestra pit, which is usually located in a lowered area in front of the stage. This is usually where all the musicians sit and play their instruments.

Nos da cariad – Welsh for 'good night love!'.

'Get in' and 'get out' – this is the process of moving the set, the props and other belongings of the show into the theatre, or moving everything out either into storage or transport for the next venue.

Wings – these are the areas both sides of the stage that are out of view of the audience.

Dock doors – the loading bay area behind the stage where the big parts of the scenery can be brought through.

Tannoy – this is the public address system that announcements can be heard through. Speakers are usually dotted all over the theatre's backstage so actors can always hear their calls, wherever they are in the building.

Flies – the fly system is lines, blocks and counterweights that the stage crew use to quickly, quietly and safely move scenery, lights, curtains, etc. and sometimes even people, down into view of the audience, and then up into a spacious lofty area above that is out of view.

Front of house – this is the area at the front of the theatre used by the public.

Green room – this is where all the workers backstage in the theatre can go to relax when they are not on stage.

Circle, stalls, 'the gods' – these are the different levels of the seating in a theatre. The stalls are the lowest, the circle is usually the middle and 'the gods' are the highest part sometimes known as the upper circle.

Dry ice – it's the white mist created on stage by frozen carbon dioxide.

Digs – this is accommodation for travelling actors located near to theatres they may be working. They are usually rented rooms, flats, or sometimes entire houses, which are often cheaper for actors than staying in hotels – which can be a bit pricey if they have to do it all the time.

ABOUT THE AUTHOR

As the daughter of two of Britain's favourite actors, Ruth and Philip Madoc, Lowri was aware her home life was a little different from that of many of her friends at boarding school.

Growing up, weekends and holidays were often spent backstage in theatres, studio audiences, and on TV and film sets. Her parents' work during the fabulous 1980s and '90s meant large parts of Lowri's formative years were spent immersed in sitcoms, gameshows, summer seasons and pantos, many classical plays, films and audio recordings, as well as various TV drama series. From 'It's a Knockout' to 'Dostoyevsky', the exposure couldn't have been more diverse.

Occasionally, but reluctantly, Lowri would be asked to get involved in front of the camera.

Funny, yet usually cringey, her credits include 'Hi-de-Hi', the gameshow 'Whose Baby?', 'This is Your Life', GMTV with 'Mad Lizzie' and a programme for the Disney Channel. Gotta love the '80s!

Not interested in the limelight, Lowri was however captivated by what went on backstage and on set.

After many hours spent with production staff and front of house teams, it was little wonder she chose a career in stage management and then theatre management. Her final venue was The Lyceum, Covent Garden, where she was part of the theatre management team for three years, playing host to two Royal Variety Performances, among other prestigious productions and occasions.

Lowri now lives in Gibraltar with her husband Brendan and their three children Riain, Lili and Dexter.

.

Printed in Great Britain
by Amazon